LUCY VAN PELT

FLAWLESS ADVICE

First published in Great Britain in 2015
by Canongate Books Ltd, 14 High Street, Edinburgh EH1 1TE

www.canongate.tv

1

Copyright © 2015 by Peanuts Worldwide LLC

The moral right of the author has been asserted

British Library Cataloguing-in-Publication Data
A catalogue record for this book is available on
request from the British Library

ISBN 978 1 78211 361 4

PEANUTS written and drawn by Charles M. Schulz
Edited by Jenny Lord
Designed by Rafaela Romaya

Printed in Latvia by Livonia Print, SIA

HOW TO BE A
GRRRL!
BY LUCY VAN PELT

CANONGATE
Edinburgh · London

A PUBLIC SERVICE ANNOUNCEMENT

FROM LUCY VAN PELT!

CHAPTER 1

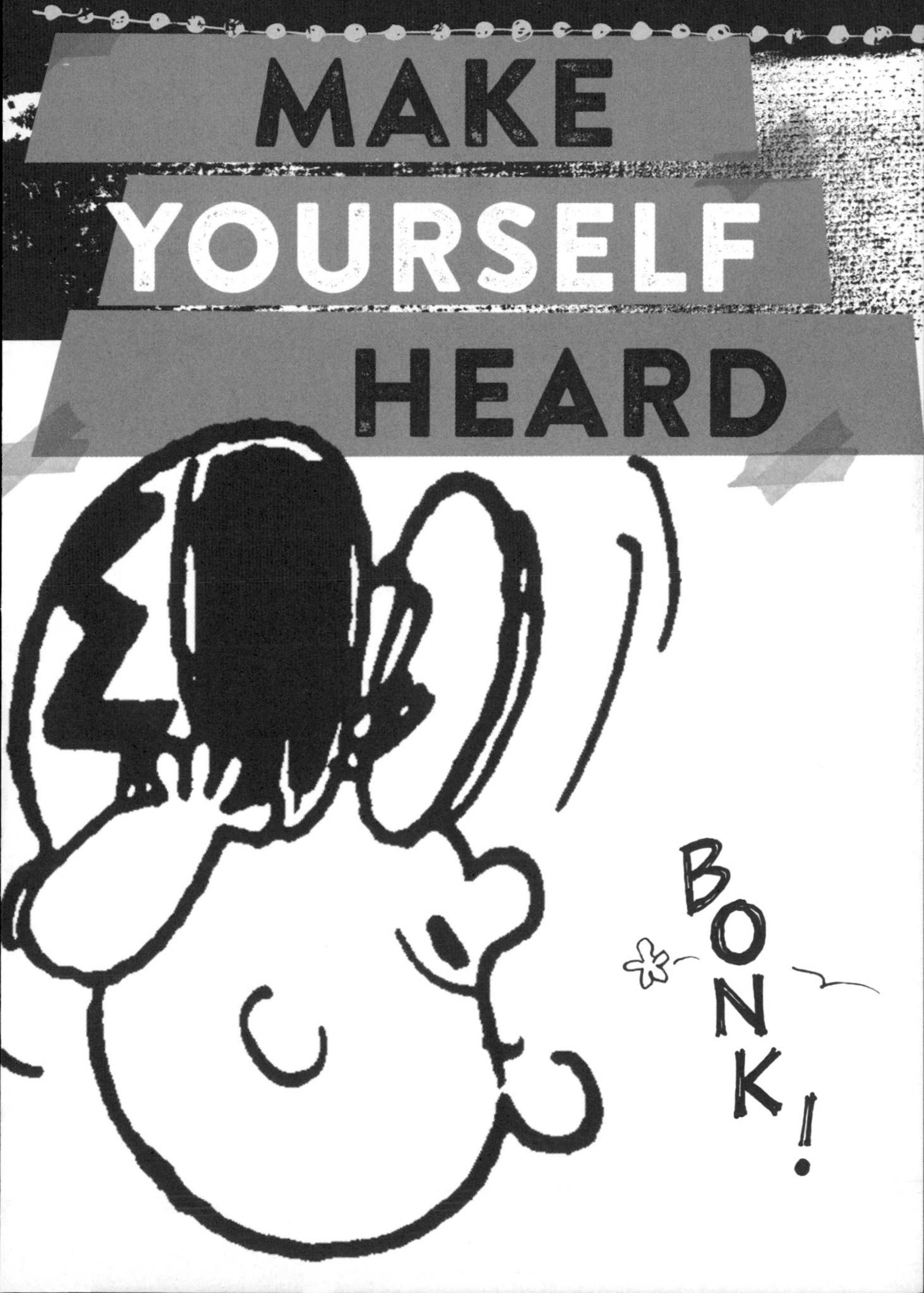
MAKE YOURSELF HEARD
BONK!

But not the mouth.

THE CRABBY
LITTLE GIRLS
OF TODAY ARE
THE CRABBY
OLD WOMEN
OF TOMORROW!

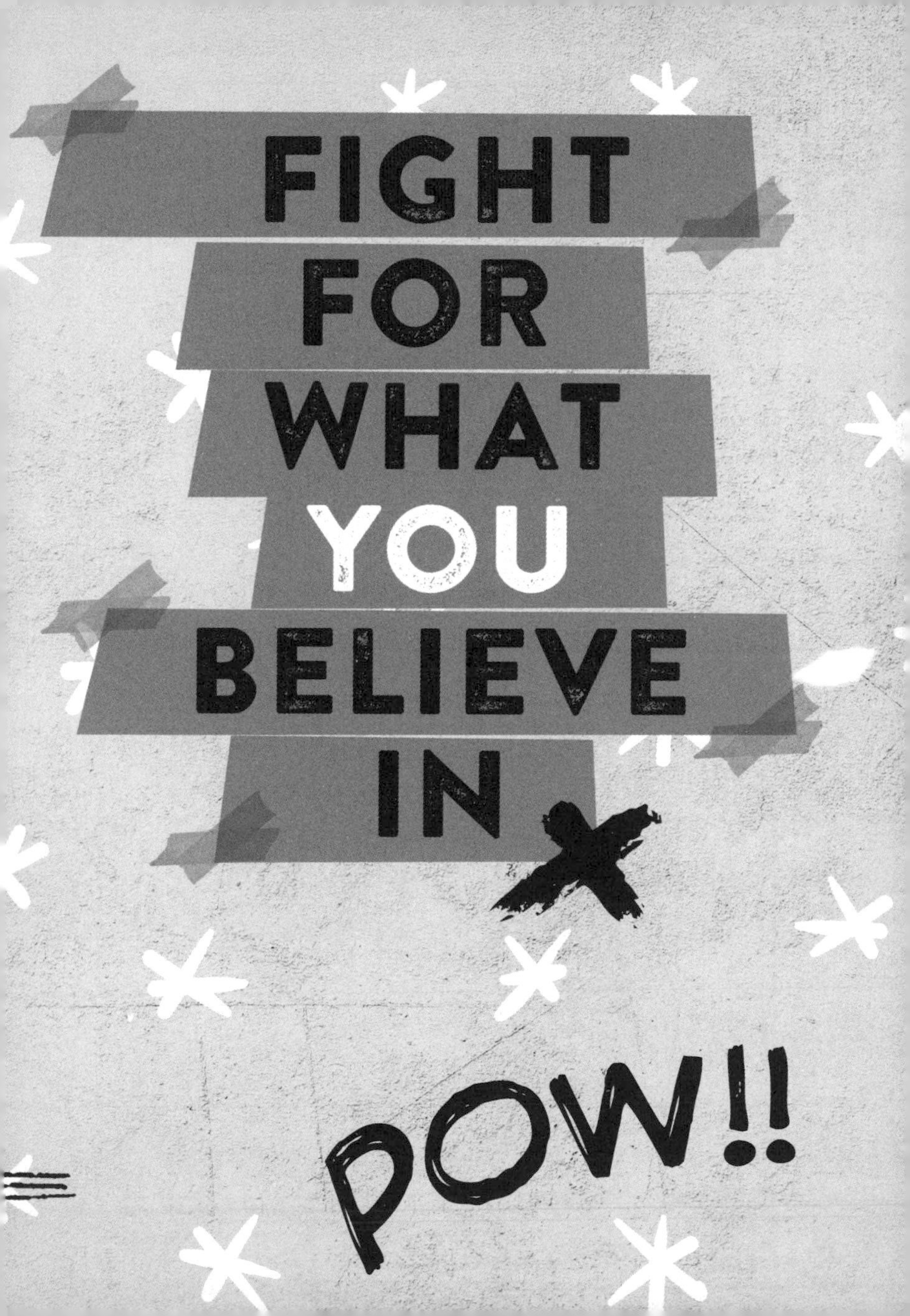
FIGHT
FOR
WHAT
YOU
BELIEVE
IN
POW!!

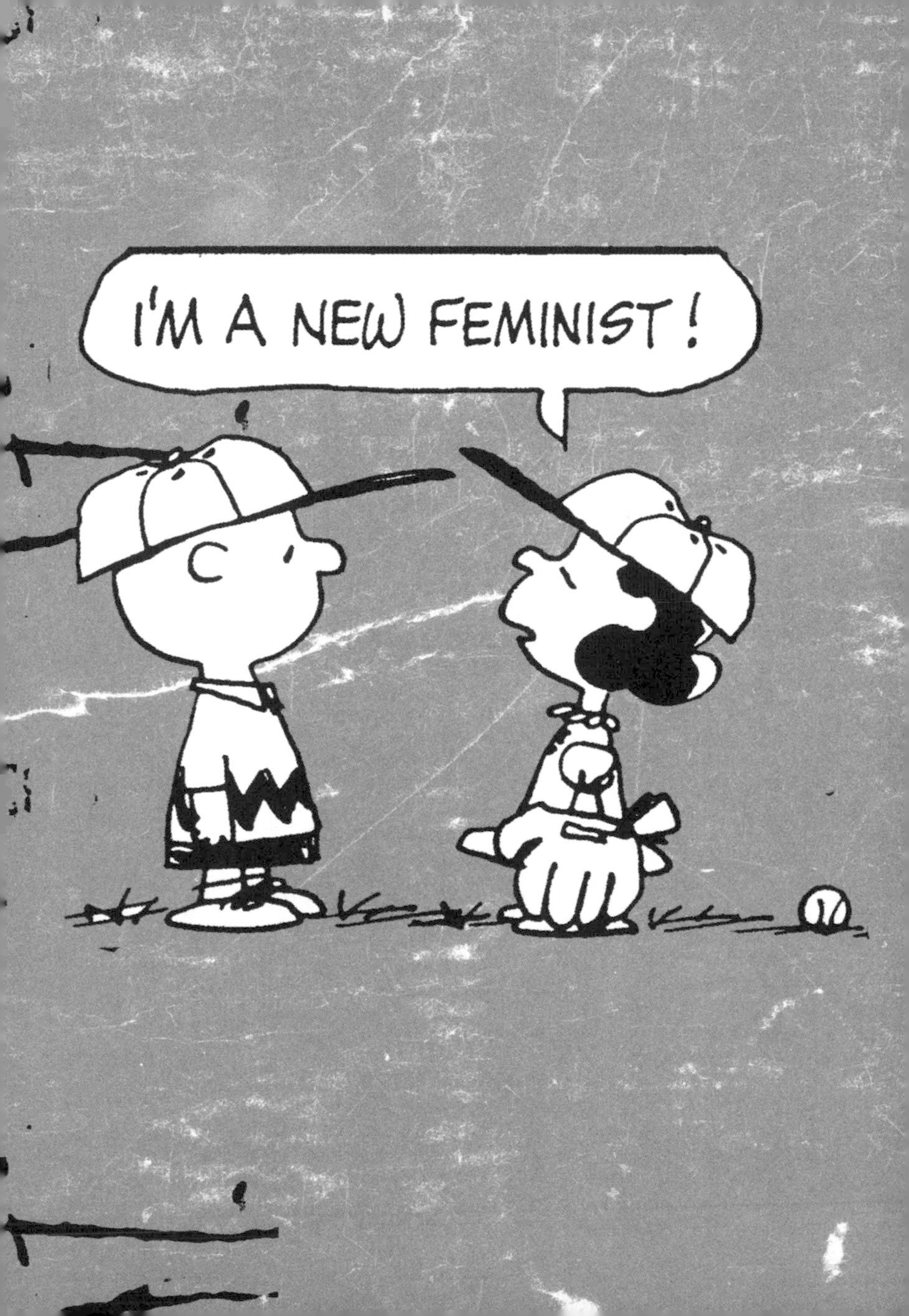
I'M A NEW FEMINIST!

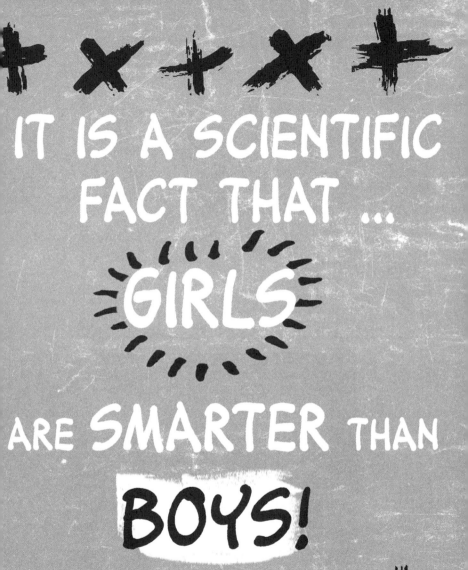

CHAPTER 4

DIRECTOR OF
EVERYTHING

ALWAYS
TAKE
CONTROL

STRIKE
ONE!

ALL RIGHT,
EVERYBODY
OUT OF MY
BEANBAG
CHAIR !!

I SAID,
EVERYBODY!

APPARENTLY SOME PEOPLE JUST DON'T LISTEN! I SAID **EVERYBODY!**

ART SHOULD BE UNCONFINED!
ART MUST HAVE FREEDOM!
COLOURING THE MANY FACES OF LUCY VAN PELT

STAND UP FOR YOUR SISTERS!

POWER TO MY KIND!

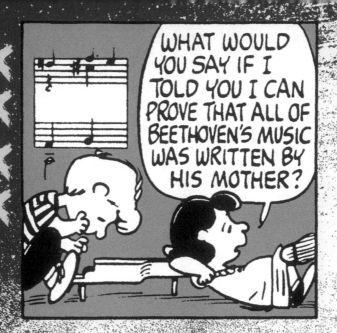

ANOTHER TRIUMPH FOR WOMEN'S LIB!

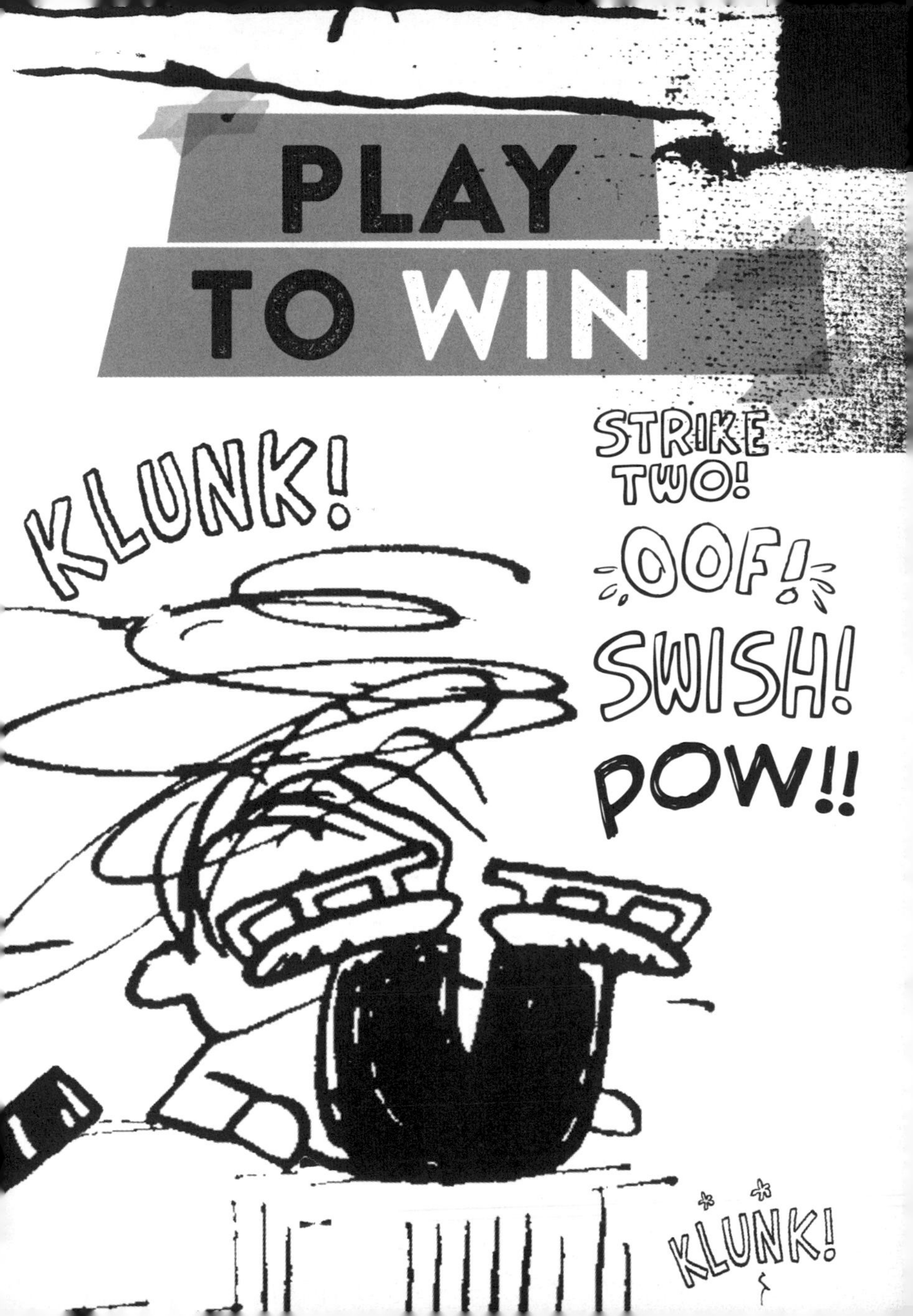
PLAY
TO WIN
STRIKE TWO!
KLUNK!
OOF!
SWISH!
POW!!
KLUNK!

ALL RIGHT, LET'S PLAY "QUEEN OF THE HILL"

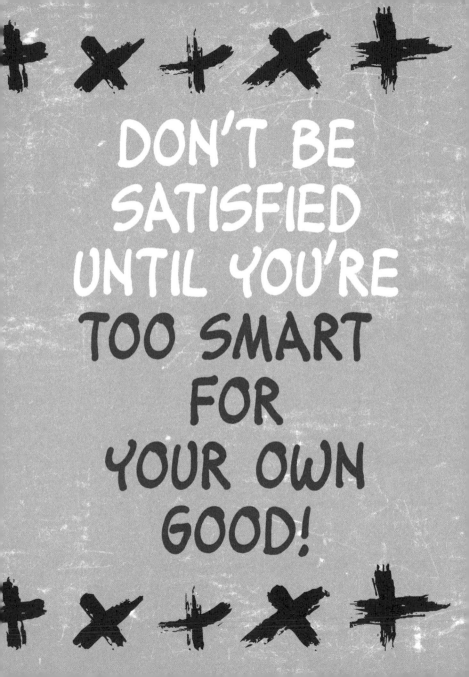

STICK UP FOR YOURSELF!

LIFE IS FULL OF CHOICES!

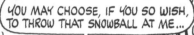

YOU MAY CHOOSE, IF YOU SO WISH, TO THROW THAT SNOWBALL AT ME...

YOU ALSO MAY CHOOSE, IF YOU SO WISH, NOT TO THROW THAT SNOWBALL AT ME...

NOW, IF YOU CHOOSE TO THROW THAT SNOWBALL AT ME, I WILL POUND YOU RIGHT INTO THE GROUND!

IF YOU CHOOSE NOT TO THROW THAT SNOWBALL AT ME, YOUR HEAD WILL BE SPARED

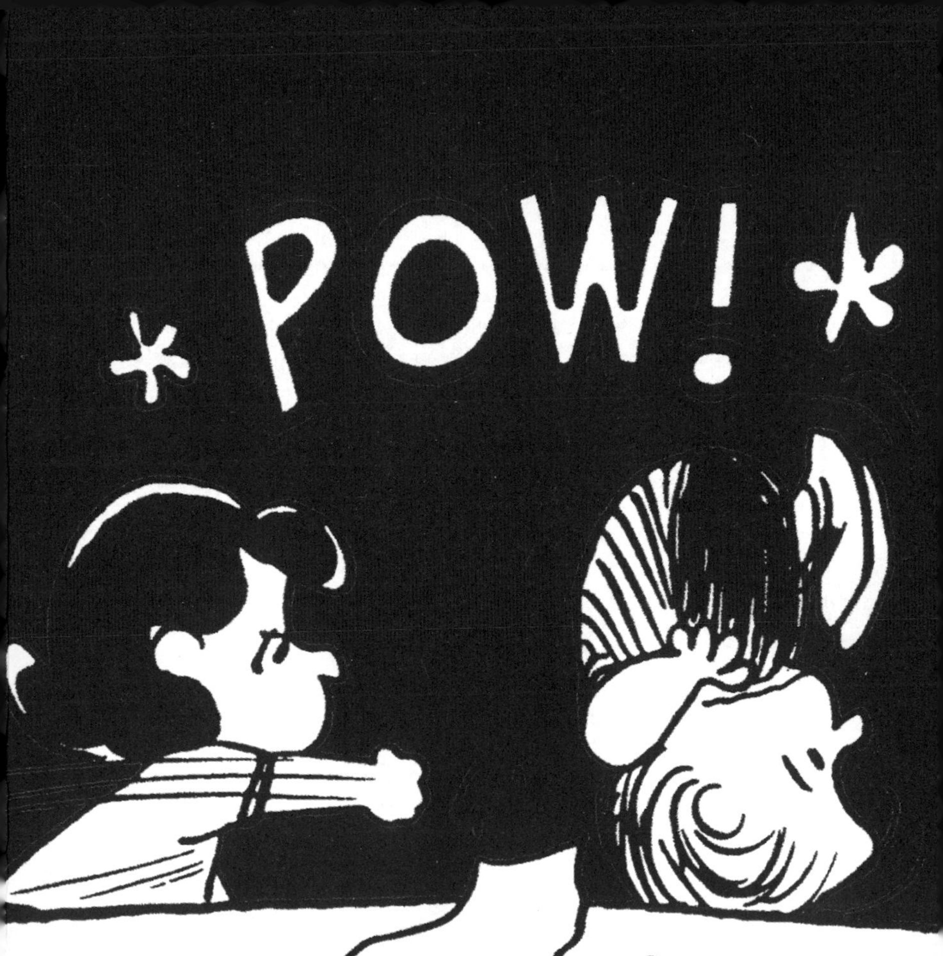
POW!

DON'T LET ANYONE WALK ALL OVER YOU!